Maths Revision Booklet
for CCEA GCSE 2-tier specification

M1

Lowry Johnston

Contents

A calculator may be used in these exercises.

Revision Exercise 1

1. **(a)** Mr and Mrs Collins are going on a cruise. The ship has space for 3076 passengers.
   Write the number of passengers to the nearest hundred.

   Answer _____

   (b) The ship has one thousand, one hundred and eighty five crew members.
   Write this in numbers.

   Answer _____

   (c) They are flying from Belfast to Barcelona. The flight leaves Belfast at 0915 and arrives in Barcelona at 1300 local time. If the time in Barcelona is 1 hour ahead of the time in Belfast, how long does the flight take?

   Answer _____

   (d) At the first port of call they will have to pay €24 for a shuttle bus ticket to the centre of the resort. If £1.00 buys €1.25, how much does the shuttle bus ticket cost in £s?

   Answer _____

2. Fifty people were asked if they liked the taste of Marmite. The two-way table shows the results.

	Liked	Disliked
Male	14	6
Female	18	

   (a) Complete the two-way table.

   (b) Complete the frequency tree from the two-way table.

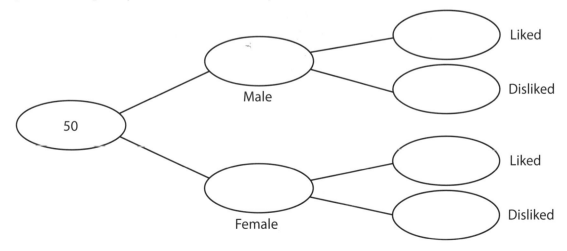

3. **(a)** Mark a point X on the circumference of the circle drawn below.

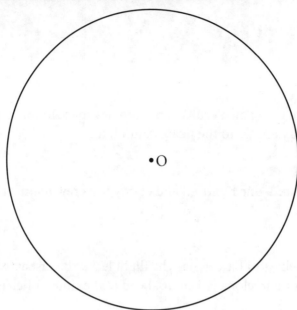

(b) Join X to O at the centre of the circle.
  (i) What is the line OX called?

Answer _____

  (ii) Measure the length of OX.

Answer _____ cm

4. The bar chart shows the **average daily temperatures** in Spain from April to October.

Average daily temperatures

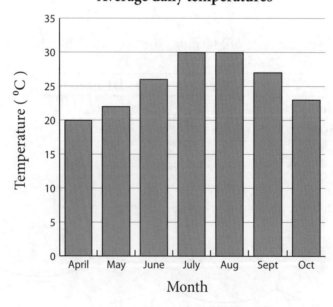

(a) Which two months have the same average daily temperature?

Answer_____and_____

(b) Which month has the lowest average daily temperature?

Answer _____

(c) What is the **range** for the average daily temperatures?

Answer _____

5. **(a)** From the numbers 11, 49, 15, 21, 33, 6, 7 write down

   (i) a square number

   Answer _____

   (ii) a multiple of 5

   Answer _____

   (iii) a factor of 54

   Answer _____

   (b) George has £5. He buys 4 packets of stickers at 60p each.
   How much change should he get?
   Show your working.

   Answer £ _____

6. **(a)** Number cards are arranged to make the number 4791 as shown below.

   | 4 | 7 | 9 | 1 |

   (i) What is the value of the 7 in this number?

   Answer _____

   (ii) Write this number to the nearest 100.

   Answer _____

   (iii) If the cards are rearranged, what is the largest number that it is possible to make?

   Answer _____

   (b) The length of a work bench is three thousand and twenty five millimetres. Write this as a number.

   Answer _____ millimetres

7. **(a)** 58 tennis balls are packed in cylindrical cartons. Each carton holds 5 tennis balls.
   (i) How many cartons will be needed?

   Answer _____

   (ii) How many cartons will be full?

   Answer _____

   (iii) What fraction of the remaining carton is filled?

   Answer _____

   (b) The £180 bill for a meal is made up as follows: 66⅔% for food, ⅙ for drinks and a £30 service charge.

   (i) What is the cost of the food?

   Answer _____

   The service charge is a percentage of the total cost of food and drink.

   (ii) What is the percentage service charge?

   Answer _____ %

8. The hourly rate for the national minimum wage is set out in the table below.

Age	25 and over	21 to 24	18 to 20	Under 18
Hourly Rate	£7.50	£7.05	£5.60	£4.05

   (a) John is 17 years old and works 20 hours per week. How much should he get paid?

   Answer _____

   (b) On Sunday he celebrates his 18ᵗʰ birthday. How much more should he be paid for working 20 hours in the week following his birthday?

   Answer _____

   (c) What is the percentage increase in the hourly rate for a person turning 25 years old?
   (Give your answer correct to one decimal place.)

   Answer _____

9.

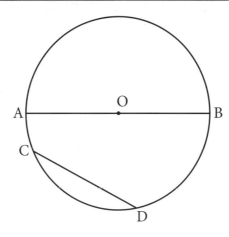

Choose from

| chord | circumference | radius | diameter | tangent |

to complete these sentences:

(a) The line AOB is called a _____.

(b) The line CD is called a _____.

10. (a) What metric unit would be used to measure:

    (i)   the length of a school corridor?

                                             Answer _____

    (ii) the amount of nail polish in a bottle?

                                             Answer _____

(b) The diagram below shows the net of a shape. Name the shape.

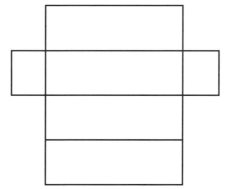

                                           Answer _____

11. (a) The measurements for some replacement worktops are 0.602 m, 0.620 m, 0.260 m and 1.060 m.

    (i) Write these measurements in ascending order.

    Answer _____

    (ii) These worktops are cut from a 3 metre length of worktop material.
    How many millimetres are left over?

                                         Answer _____ mm

(b) From the list of test results

    8, 5, 6, 8, 7, 4, 7, 8, 5, 9, 8, 2, 9, 7, 8

    find:

    (i) the mode

                                        Answer _____

    (ii) the median

                                        Answer _____

(c) Michael scored 62% in a Maths test. The median for Michael's class was 64%. Describe how well Michael did.

    Answer _____

    _____

    _____

    _____

12. (a) The printer has accidentally left the brackets out of the following calculations.
Insert the brackets where they should have been printed.

    (i) $12 \div 2 + 4 = 2$

    (ii) $5 + 4 \times 2 = 18$

    (iii) $6 \times 7 - 12 \div 5 - 2 = 10$

(b) Complete the blanks for the following function machine.

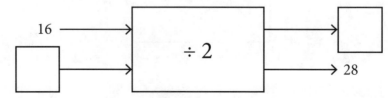

(c) 54 385 people attended a Cup Final. Write this number correct to the nearest 100.

                                        Answer _____

13. An athletics coach recorded a sprinter's finishing position in her last 36 races.

Position	1st	2nd	3rd	4th	5th
Frequency	2	5	7	10	12

On the grid below, draw a bar chart to show this information.

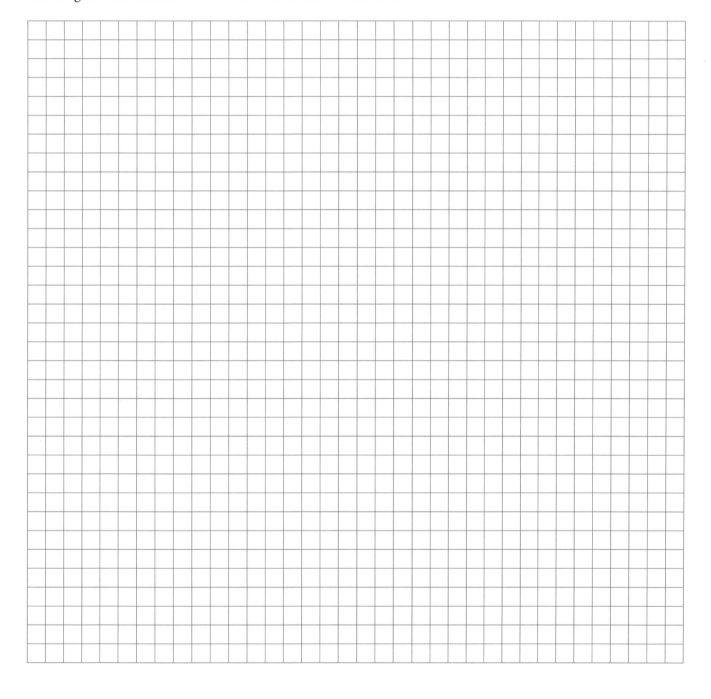

Revision Exercise 2

1. 75 people were asked which music they liked best. The first three rows of the pictogram are drawn below.

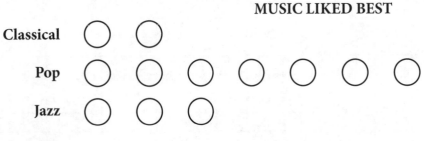

MUSIC LIKED BEST

(a) 10 people liked **Classical** music best.

Complete the key: ◯ = _____ people

(b) How many people liked **Pop** music best?

Answer _____

(c) Complete the row of the pictogram for **Other** music.

2. The tables below shows the flights from Belfast to London Stansted and return with their prices.

Belfast to London Stansted

2 November		3 November		4 November	
Dep. 0610	£25.49	Dep. 0920	£36.49	Dep. 0610	£22.49
Dep. 1410	£32.49	Dep. 1410	£25.49		
Dep. 1820	£22.49	Dep. 1820	£22.49	Dep. 1955	£22.49

London Stansted to Belfast

3 November		4 November		5 November	
Dep. 0735	£33.49	Dep. 0750	£39.49	Dep. 1240	£47.49
Dep. 1415	£42.49			Dep. 1455	£44.49
Dep. 1820	£53.49	Dep. 18.10	£49.49	Dep. 1940	£47.49

(a) What is the cost of the cheapest way to fly to London Stansted on 3 November and returning on 4 November?

Answer _____

(b) What is the cost of the most expensive way to fly to London Stansted on 3 November and returning on 4 November?

Answer _____

(c) Explain why you would not choose the cheapest way to fly to London on 3 November and returning on 4 November.

Answer _____

_____

_____

(d) Find another set of flights (other than the cheapest or dearest) which would best suit travelling to London Stansted on 3 November and returning on 4 November. Justify your answer.

Answer _____

Justification _____

_____

_____

3. (a) Mary's grandpa was 79 years old on 12 September 2008. In what year was he born?

Answer _____

(b) Write down all the factors of 18.

Answer _____

(c) 400 tickets were printed for a Bangor Ladies' Choir concert.
127 tickets remain to be sold. How many were sold?

Answer _____

4.

A

B

C

D

E

F

G

H

I

J

(a) Name two pairs of congruent shapes.

Answer _____ and _____

Answer _____ and _____

(b) Choose from

square	rhombus	rectangle	kite
trapezium	pentagon	parallelogram	

to complete the sentences.

(i) Shape A is a _____

(ii) Shape B is a _____

(iii) Shape C is a _____

5.

A ————————————————————— B

(a) Measure the length of the line AB.

Answer AB = _____

(b) Using AB as the base, construct a triangle ABC. The length of AC is 6 cm and CAB is a right angle.

(c) Measure the length of the line BC.

Answer BC = _____

6. The cuboid show below is made up of 1 cm cubes.

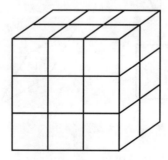

What is the volume of the cuboid?

Answer _____ cm³

7. **(a)** A tourist is facing in the direction of a tower which is due north of him.

N

(i) He makes a ¼ turn clockwise. In what direction is he now facing?

Answer _____

(ii) He makes a further ½ turn clockwise. In what direction is he now facing?

Answer _____

(iii) How much further clockwise does he need to turn to face North again?

Answer _____

(b) The diagram below show parallel railway tracks crossing a road at a point where the road is getting wider.

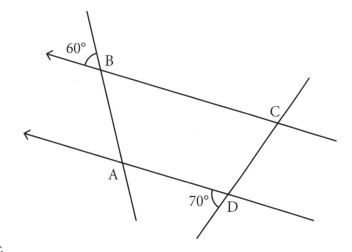

(i) Find the size of:

∠DCB = _____ °

∠CBA = _____ °

∠BAD = _____ °

∠ADC = _____ °

(ii) How could you check to see if your answers are correct?

Answer _____

_____

8. As an incentive to use a credit card, 1 *UR-point* is awarded for each 50p spent.
   Neil's use of his credit card has earned him 27 077 *UR-points*.
   He investigates using them to pay for return flights to London for his wife and himself.

   (a) If they take 2 suitcases 33 100 *UR-points* are required.

   (i) How many *UR-points* does he still need to collect?

   Answer _____

   (ii) How much does this require him to spend using his credit card?

   Answer £ _____

   (b) If they take only 1 suitcase then 25 900 *UR-points* are required.
   How many *UR-points* are saved by taking only 1 suitcase?

   Answer _____

   (c) Using money it costs £18 to take a suitcase.
   Approximately how many *UR-points* are equivalent to £1?

   Answer _____

9. Calls from a hotel room are charged at the following rate per minute.

   Local call   **50p**

   Mobile call   **£2.50**

   Europe   **£3.50**

   USA   **£5.50**

   (a) Mary made a call lasting 12 minutes to Paris in Europe. How much did this add to her bill?

   Answer _____

   (b) Malcolm made a 4 minute call to the USA, a 4 minute call to Europe and a mobile call. This added £51 to his bill. For how many minutes did he make a call to a mobile?

   Answer _____

10. (a) 1250 mm are cut from a 2 m length of skirting board. What length is left?

Answer _____ mm

(b) 492 eggs are packed into cartons. Each carton holds 6 eggs. How many cartons will be needed?

Answer _____

(c) Write 32 out of 200 as a percentage.

Answer _____ %

11. (a)

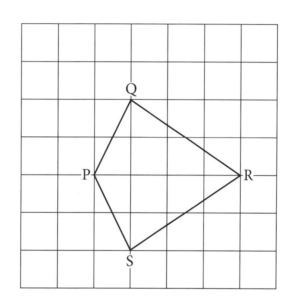

(i) Find the area of PQRS.

Answer _____ units²

(ii) Name the shape PQRS.

Answer _____

(b) Find the perimeter of the shape below, made from 1 cm squares.

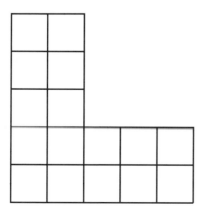

Answer _____ cm

12. O is the centre of the circle drawn below.

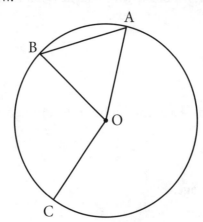

(Diagram not drawn to scale)

(a) Choose from

| acute | isosceles | scalene | obtuse | equilateral | right angled |

to complete the sentences.

(i) Angle BOC is _____

(ii) Angle AOB is _____

(b) If OAB is 60° then what type of triangle is AOB?

Answer _____

13. (a) For each type of data in the table below, put a tick in the correct column to indicate whether the type of data is discrete, continuous or categorical.

Data	Discrete	Continuous	Categorical
Weights			
Names			
Car number plates			
Age			
Class size			
Speeds			
Votes in a talent contest			
Phone numbers			
Temperatures			
Lengths			

(b) A TV broadcaster is considering if it should give free TV licences to over 75 year olds.
To gauge opinion, a sample of 100 people over 75 years old are asked their opinion about the proposal.
Make two comments about the sample.

Comment 1: _____

_____

Comment 2: _____

_____

Revision Exercise 3

1.

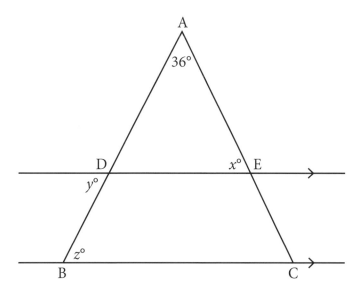

ADE is an isosceles triangle with AD = AE.
DE is parallel to BC.

(a) Calculate the size of angle

   (i) $x° = $ _____

   (ii) $y° = $ _____

   (iii) $z° = $ _____

(b) (i)   What type of triangle is ABC?

                                                            Answer _____

   (ii) Give a reason for your answer.

    Answer _____

    _____

    _____

    _____

2. Michaela was driving along a stretch of road which had an average speed limit of 40 mph. The speeds of the cars are checked using speed cameras which are placed 1 mile apart. She drove the first ½ mile at 60 mph. What was her maximum speed over the next ½ mile if she just avoided going over the 40 mph average speed limit?

                                                             Answer _____

3. **(a)** Solve the equations:
   (i) $7x = 21$

   Answer _____

   (ii) $x + 5 = 13$

   Answer _____

   (b) Simplify $3a + a + 6a$

   Answer _____

   (c) Expand $3(x + 5)$

   Answer _____

4. The formula used to convert the temperature in degrees Fahrenheit (°F) to degrees Celsius (°C) is

   $$°C = (°F - 32) \times \frac{5}{9}$$

   Use this formula to work out:
   (a) The equivalent of 68°F in °C.

   Answer _____

   (b) The equivalent of 30°C in °F.

   Answer _____

5. **(a)** Write down
   (i) the value of 8.5^2

   Answer _____

   (ii) the value of $\sqrt{1.69}$

   Answer _____

   (b) At 6 am the temperature in New York is −7°C. At midday it is 1°C.
   By how much has the temperature risen?

   Answer _____°C

6. James wants to put a circular fish pond in his garden.

The diameter of the pond is 1.8 m.

(a) Calculate the area of the pond. (Give your answer correct to one decimal place.)

Answer _____ m²

(b) Calculate the perimeter of the pond. (Give your answer to the nearest whole number.)

Answer _____ m

7. **(a)** *Dancing on Ice: the Skate Off* starts at 8.50 pm. What is this time on a 24 hour clock?

Answer _____

(b) Write 80% as a decimal.

Answer _____

(c) Write 17 out of 20 as a percentage.

Answer _____ %

(d) Calculate

    (i) 7% of £800

Answer _____

    (ii) 70% of £50

Answer _____

8. Fifteen pupils estimated the size of an angle drawn on a page.
The information is shown in a stem and leaf diagram below.

Angle Estimates

```
5 | 1 1 3
4 | 2 2 6 6 6 8
3 | 1 3 4 7
2 | 7 9
```

2 | 7 means 27°

(a) What is the largest estimate?

Answer _____

(b) What estimate is the mode?

Answer _____

(c) What estimate is the median?

Answer _____

(d) The actual size of the angle is 47°. How many pupils estimated less than the size of the angle?

Answer _____ pupils

9. **(a)** Solve the equations:
   (i) $19 - x = 14$

Answer $x =$ _____

   (ii) $\frac{x}{4} = 8$

Answer $x =$ _____

   (iii) $4x - 3 = 9$

Answer $x =$ _____

(b) Expand
   $3(2x + 5)$

Answer _____

10. A multiple choice paper is marked as follows:

3 marks for a correct answer (✔)

−2 marks for an incorrect answer (✘)

−1 mark when there is no attempt to answer question (−)

Claire's Attempt

Question Number	1	2	3	4	5	6	7	8	9	10
	✔	✔	✘	✘	−	✔	−	✔	✘	✔
Marks	3	3	−2	−2	−1					

(a) Complete the table of marks and find Claire's score.

Answer _____

(b) John scored −2

(i) How many marks difference is there between John's score and Claire's score?

Answer _____

(ii) John got no questions incorrect. How many did he attempt?

Answer _____

(iii) Describe another way to score −2

Answer _____

_____

11.

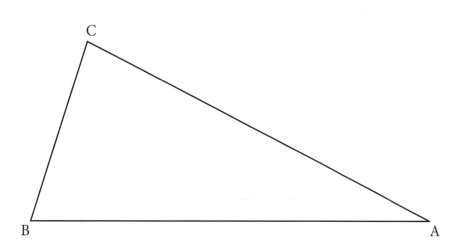

(a) Measure the angle B.

Answer _____ °

(b)

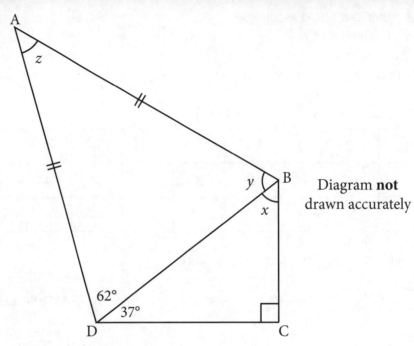

Diagram **not** drawn accurately

ABD is an isosceles triangle with AB = AD.
BCD is a right angled triangle.
Calculate the size of angle:

(i) x

Answer _____ °

(ii) y

Answer _____ °

(iii) z

Answer _____ °

12. Grace has chosen a car to buy. The salesperson offers her two options for paying for it over 36 months.

Option 1 (PCP)	
Deposit	£1030.00
First Payment	£231.49
35 Monthly Payments	£221.49
Final Payment	£4016.50

Option 2 (HP)	
Deposit	£1030.00
First Payment	£322.02
35 Monthly Payments	£312.02
Final Payment	£0.00

Which of the two options will cost less over the 36 months and by how much?

Answer Option _____ by £ _____

13. (a) Kevin bought a magazine costing £1.55 and a bottle of cola costing £1.08
    (i)   What was the total cost of the two items?

Answer _____

    (ii) How much change did he get from £5?

Answer _____

   (b) Write down
    (i)   the value of the cube root of 27;

Answer _____

    (ii) both values of the square root of 36.

Answer _____ , _____

14. Fifty stray pets were checked to see if they had been fitted with an identity chip. They were a mixture of dogs and cats. The two-way table shows the results.

	Chipped	Not chipped
Dog	14	5
Cat		21

(a) Complete the two-way table.

(b) Complete the frequency tree from the two-way table.

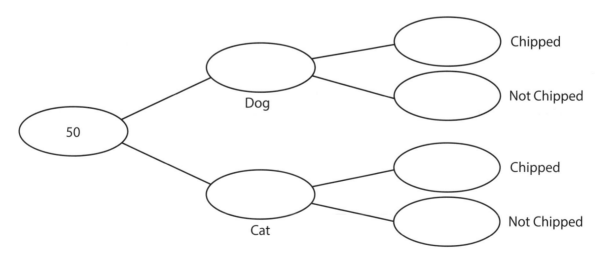

Revision Exercise 4

1. The diagram below shows the distances between various towns in Northern Ireland.

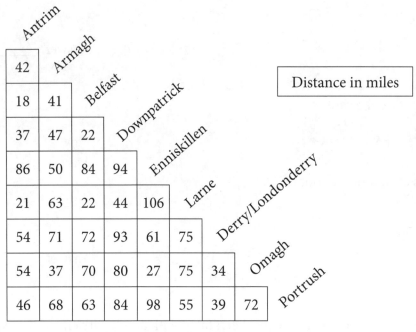

(a) Which two towns are the greatest distance apart?

Answer _____ and _____

(b) The distance from Belfast to Enniskillen is 84 miles. Which other two towns are 84 miles apart?

Answer _____ and _____

(c) Jean drives from Armagh to Enniskillen and back to Armagh. How many miles is this?

Answer _____ miles

2. (a) The lights for a Christmas tree are 3 different colours. There are red lights which flash every 2 seconds, blue lights which flash every 3 seconds and yellow lights which flash every 4 seconds. After how many seconds will all three coloured lights flash at the same time?

Answer _____

(b) Expand and simplify $5(2c - 3) + 2(3c - 2)$

Answer _____

3. **(a)** Solve the equation
   $3x + 7 = 19$

   Answer _____

   (b) Factorise $6a - 27$

   Answer _____

   (c) Expand
   $-5(x + 2)$

   Answer _____

4. **(a)**

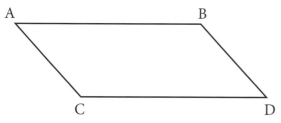

ABCD is a parallelogram.
The length of AB is 2cm more than the length of BD.
The perimeter of the parallelogram is 40 cm.
Let the length of BD = x.
Write down an equation in x and use it to work out the length of AB.

Equation in x _____

Answer AB = _____ cm

   (b) The price of a laptop is £300 + £60 VAT
   What is the VAT percentage rate?

   Answer _____ %

5. **(a)** Simplify $3a - 2b - b + 7a$

   Answer _____

   (b) Solve $17 - x = 9$

   Answer $x =$ _____

   (c) Factorise $25 - 10b$

   Answer _____

6. (a) The largest possible circular discs for a board game are cut out of squares of plastic of area 0.81 cm²

What is the area of material which remains? (Give your answer correct to two decimal places.)

Answer _____ cm²

(b) Mary bought 4 packets of chewing gum at 38p each.

(i) How much in total did the 4 packets cost?

Answer £ _____

(ii) How much change did she get from £5?

Answer £ _____

(c) What decimal is equivalent to $\frac{5}{100}$?

Answer _____

7. (a) Simplify
$4a + 5b - a - 3b$

Answer _____

(b) Expand
$x(x - 3)$

Answer _____

8. Name the following quadrilaterals.

(a) All its sides are equal but it has no right angles.

Answer _____

(b) It has no lines of symmetry.

Answer _____

(c) It has only one pair of parallel sides.

Answer _____

(d) It has just one line of symmetry.

Answer _____

(e) It has just one pair of opposite angles which are equal.

Answer _____

(f) It has four lines of symmetry.

Answer _____

(g) It has only half turn symmetry.

Answer _____

(h) They both have 2 lines of symmetry.

Answer _____ , _____

9. Plot the points (2, –1) and (–3, 0) on the grid below.

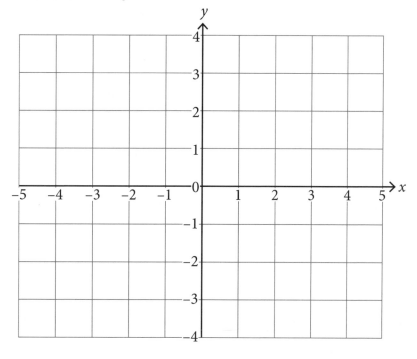

10. On the grid below, draw a net of the prism shown.

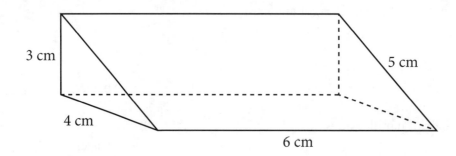

11. (a) Calculate the volume of a cuboid with dimensions 5 cm, 6 cm and 8 cm.

Answer _____ cm²

(b) Another cuboid has the same volume as this one. The area of its base is 80 cm². What is its height?

Answer _____ cm

12. (a)

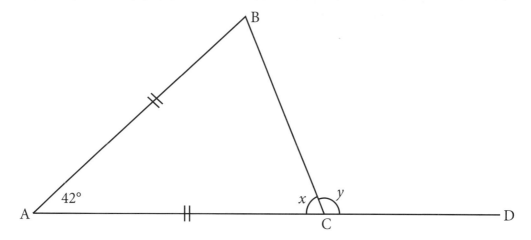

ACD is a straight line.
AB = AC.

Calculate the size of angle:

(i) *x*

Answer *x* = _____ °

(ii) *y*

Answer *y* = _____ °

(b)

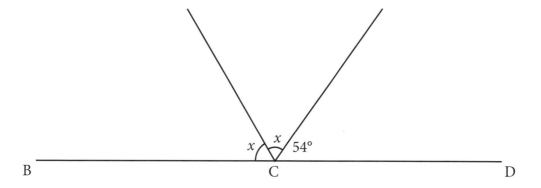

BCD is a straight line.
Calculate the value of *x*.

Answer *x* = _____ °

13. The graph below shows the distance, D (miles) a cyclist travels during a day.

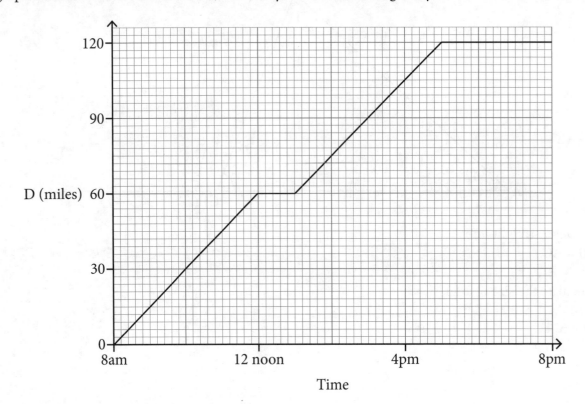

Time

(a) What time did the cyclist first stop?

Answer _____

(b) How long did the cyclist stop for?

Answer _____

(c) How far had the cyclist travelled at 3pm?

Answer _____

(d) What time did the cyclist stop for the day?

Answer _____

14. From the list of numbers

21, 32, 47, 81, 64, 16, 95, 79, 15

write down:

(a) two prime numbers;

Answer _____ and _____

(b) a cube number.

Answer _____

Revision Exercise 5

1. **(a)** Complete the following shopping bill.

   2.5 kg new potatoes at 84p per kg   _____

   3 litres of milk at £1.05 per litre   _____

   0.25 kg tomatoes at £1.64 per kg   _____

   Total £   _____

   (b) £10 is used to pay for the shopping. What is the change?

   Answer £ _____

   (c) 1 saver point is awarded for each £1 spent. How many saver points are earned when buying these 3 items?

   Answer _____

2.

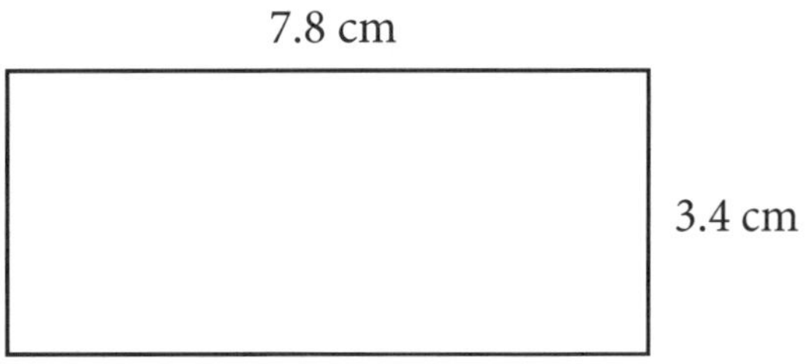

   7.8 cm

   3.4 cm

   (a) Find the area of the rectangle drawn above.

   Answer _____ cm^2

   (b) Find the perimeter of the rectangle drawn above.

   Answer _____ cm

3. (a) Find
    (i) $\sqrt{2.25}$

    Answer _____

    (ii) 3.3^2

    Answer _____

    (b) Calculate
    $2.9^2 - 3.5$

    Answer _____

    (c) An iPhone is priced at £150. In a sale, 20% discount is given.
        How much is the discount?

    Answer £ _____

4. (a) The cost of hiring a carpet cleaner is £15.75 plus £4.25 per day.
        How much does it cost to hire the carpet cleaner for 3 days?

    Answer £ _____

    (b) Another hire company charges £22.75 for the first day and £2.25 for each additional day.
        Mrs Todd pays £34 for the hire of the carpet cleaner.

        For how many days did she hire this carpet cleaner?

    Answer _____ days

5. (a) Lorraine pays £1.75 for 0.4 kg of green grapes and 0.5 kg of black grapes.
        The green grapes cost £1.85 per kg.

        How much are the black grapes per kg?

    Answer £ _____

    (b) Myla earns £14 000 per year. On 1 April 2008 she is due to get a 3% pay rise.

        How much is this pay rise per year?

    Answer £ _____

6. Pupils choose the following to drink at break time.

Break Time Drink

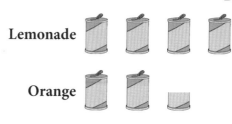

Lemonade

Orange

Coke

Water

(a) 16 pupils choose lemonade. Complete the scale key.

 means _____ pupils

(b) How many pupils choose orange?

Answer _____ pupils

(c) 24 pupils choose coke. Complete the pictogram.

7. The speeds (in miles per hour) of cars passing a school entrance are listed below.

41 29 31 28 35 31 37 40 45 50
25 32 37 51 47 48 21 25 34 39
42 34 55 24 26 34 42 46 21 23

(a) Complete the tally table below for these speeds.

Speed	Tally	Number
21 – 30		
31 – 40		
41 – 50		
51 – 60		

(b) The speed limit is 30 mph. What is the percentage of cars that are exceeding the speed limit?

Answer _____ %

8. Some teenagers were asked the type of movie they liked best. The results are shown below.

Horror	20%
Action	35%
Comedy	25%
Love	5%
Science Fiction	15%

Use the circle to draw a pie chart to show this information.

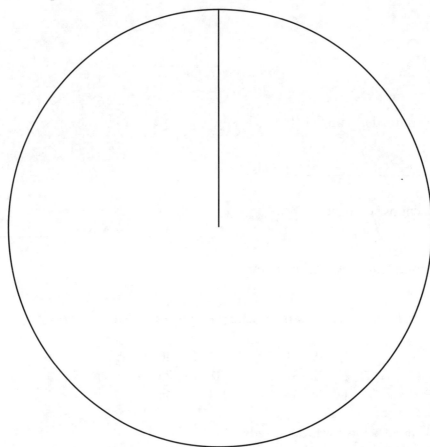

9. Oil cost 50p per litre when Mrs Gaw last bought 900 litres. Since then, the price of oil has gone up by 8%.
    She is due a delivery of 900 litres.
    How much should she expect to pay for it?

Answer £ _____

10. On holiday Siobhan is looking for some souvenirs to bring home to her friends.
She spots some fridge magnets at 85p each.

(a) How many can she buy for £10?

Answer _____

(b) How much change should she get?

Answer _____

11. Parts of an electricity bill are shown below.

Balance at previous bill	– £ 76.91
Payments received up to 1 February 2019	£207.00

(a) Calculate the amount in credit at 1 February 2019.

Answer £ _____

(b) Meter reading date	Present Reading	Previous Reading	Units Used	Units Price (pence)	Tariff Description
21 February 2018	57105	54742		11.02	Home Energy

(i) Complete the table above for the number of units used.

(ii) Calculate the cost to the nearest penny of the units used.

Answer £ _____

(c) The cost of the units used by Mr and Mrs Luke is £160.

Calculate the
(i) VAT at 5% on the cost of the units used;

Answer £ _____

(ii) total cost of the electricity used including the VAT.

Answer £ _____

12. **(a)** A bowling club has 56 members. Thirty five of these are men.
What fraction are men? (Give your answer in its lowest terms.)

Answer _____

(b) A school has 300 pupils. On Friday 270 pupils were present.
What percentage was present?

Answer _____ %

(c) A jug contains 500 ml of juice. ⅕ of the juice is poured into a glass and ¼ of the juice is poured into another glass.
What fraction of juice is left in the jug? (Give your answer in its lowest terms.)

Answer _____

13. **(a)** Mrs Jay shares paying the bills with her husband.

She sets up the following monthly direct debits from her bank account.

Electricity	£35.00
Rates	£67.54
TV Licence	£14.55
TV, broadband and phone	£44.00
Car insurance	£42.23
Heating oil	£80.00

What is the total cost of these direct debits?

Answer £ _____

(b) Each month her take-home pay is £1066.37
She saves £150 and puts aside £80 for petrol and £320 to buy food.
How much is left over for spending on other things?

Answer £ _____

14. (a) Buses on Route A leave the City Hall every 15 minutes and buses on Route B leave from the same place every 18 minutes. The first Route A and Route B buses leave the City Hall together at 8.00 am. When will be the next time that the Route A and Route B buses leave the City Hall together?

Answer _____

(b) List the common factors of 42 and 70.

Answer _____

(c) Sort the following numbers by placing them in the correct space in the Venn diagram.

8, 9, 10, 11, 15, 20, 27, 30

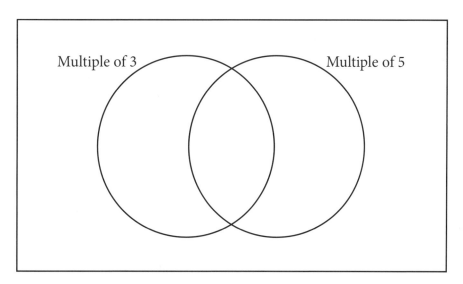

(d) Of the 936 boys and girls attending a concert 624 were girls.

(i) Find, in its lowest terms, the fraction attending the concert who were girls.

Answer _____

(ii) Write the number of boys attending the concert to the nearest ten.

Answer _____

Answers

Revision Exercise 1

1. **(a)** 3100 **(b)** 1185 **(c)** 1300 Barcelona time = 1200 Belfast time. So 2 hours 45 minutes **(d)** 24 ÷ 1. 25 = £19.20

2. **(a)**

	Liked	Disliked
Male	14	6
Female	18	12

(b)

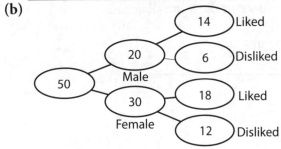

3. **(a)** point X marked anywhere on the circumference. **(b) (i)** radius **(ii)** 4 ± 0.2

4. **(a)** July and August **(b)** April **(c)** 30 – 20 = 10°C

5. **(a) (i)** 49 **(ii)** 15 **(iii)** 6
   (b) 4 × 60p = 240p = £2.40; £5.00 – £2.40 = £2.60

6. **(a) (i)** 7 hundred **(ii)** 4800 **(iii)** 9741 **(b)** 3025

7. **(a) (i)** 58 ÷ 5 = 11.6, so 12 cartons needed **(ii)** 11 **(iii)** 11.6 – 11 = 0.6 or ⅗ **(b) (i)** 66⅔% = ⅔; ⅔ × £180 = £120 **(ii)** Food + drink = 180 – 30 = 150; 30 ÷ 150 = 0.2 = 20%

8. **(a)** 4.05 × 20 = £81 **(b)** 5.60 × 20 = £112; 112 – 81 = £31 **(c)** 7.50 – 7.05 = 0.45; 0.45 ÷ 7.05 = 0.0638 = 6.4% to one decimal place

9. **(a)** diameter **(b)** chord

10. **(a) (i)** metres **(ii)** millilitres **(b)** cuboid

11. **(a) (i)** 0.260, 0.602, 0.620, 1.060 **(ii)** Total of all 4 lengths = 2.542 m; 3 –2.542 = 0.458 m = 458 mm
    (b) (i) 8
    (ii) First write them in order, giving median = 7
    (c) Michael scored a mark in the bottom half of the class when marks are put in rank order. More than half of his class scored better results.

12. **(a) (i)** 12 ÷ (2 + 4) = 2 **(ii)** (5 + 4) × 2 = 18
    (iii) (6 × 7 – 12) ÷ (5 – 2) = 10
    (b) Output 8, Input 56 **(c)** 54 400

13. Bar chart accurately drawn with axes labelled.

Revision Exercise 2

1. **(a)** 10 people ÷ 2 circles = 5 people **(b)** 7 × 5 = 35 **(c)** 12 dots already shown × 5 = 60 people; so there are 75 – 60 = 15 'Other' people; 15 ÷ 5 = 3 circles drawn opposite 'Other'

2. **(a)** 22.49 + 39.49 = £61.98 **(b)** 36.49 + 49.49 = £85.98 **(c)** going out on the 1820 and returning on the 0750 would just about give enough time for a sleep. **(d)** Going out on the 1410, returning on the 1810 gives over a day in London and costs £74.98 which is about mid-way between the cheapest and the dearest price.

3. **(a)** 2008 – 79 = 1929 **(b)** 1, 2, 3, 6, 9,18 in any order **(c)** 400 – 127 = 273

4. **(a)** A and H; E and I **(b) (i)** Rectangle **(ii)** Trapezium **(iii)** Parallelogram

5. **(a)** 8 cm **(b)** accurate right angled triangle, A = 90° **(c)** 10 cm ± 1 mm

6. 2 × 3 × 3 = 18 cm³

7. **(a) (i)** east **(ii)** west **(iii)** ¼ turn or 90° **(b) (i)** 70° since AD and BC are parallel; 60° by opposite angles; 180 – 60 = 120°, 180 – 80 = 110° **(ii)** check that they add up to 360°

8. **(a) (i)** 33100 – 27077 = 6023
   (ii) 6023 × £0.50 = £3011.50
   (b) 33100 – 25900 = 7200 **(c)** 7200 ÷ 18 = 400

9. **(a)** 12 × £3.50 = £42 **(b)** USA call = 4 × 5.50 = £22; Europe call = 4 × 3.50 = £14; 51 – (22 + 14) = £15 on a mobile call; 15 ÷ 2.50 = 6 minutes

10. **(a)** 2 m = 2000 mm; 2000 – 1250 = 750 mm
    (b) 492 ÷ 6 = 82 **(c)** 32 ÷ 200 × 100% = 16%

11. **(a) (i)** Area of triangle PQR = ½ × 4 × 2 = 4 units²; area of PSR also = 4 units²; area of PQRS = 4 + 4 = 8 units² **(ii)** Kite **(b)** 20

12. **(a) (i)** Obtuse **(ii)** Acute **(b)** Equilateral

13. (a)

Data	Dis.	Con.	Cat.
Weights		✓	
Names			✓
Car number plates			✓
Age	✓		
Class size	✓		
Speeds		✓	
Votes in a talent contest	✓		
Phone numbers			✓
Temperatures		✓	
Lengths		✓	

(b) The sample size of 100 is too small. Opinions are likely to be biased since everyone in the sample is in the group that stands to benefit.

Revision Exercise 3

1. **(a) (i)** $36 + x + x = 180$; giving $x = 72°$ **(ii)** $72°$ as x and y are opposite angles **(iii)** $72°$ as z and x are corresponding angles **(b) (i)** Isosceles **(ii)** because the base angles are both equal to $72°$ as AED and ACB are corresponding angles.

2. Let her new speed $= x$; $(½ × 60) + (½x) = 40$; giving $x = 20$ mph

3. **(a) (i)** $x = 21 ÷ 7 = 3$ **(ii)** $x = 13 - 5 = 8$
   (b) $10a$ **(c)** $3x + 15$

4. **(a)** C $= (68 - 32) × \frac{5}{9} = 20°$C **(b)** $30 = (F - 32) × \frac{5}{9}$; so $54 = F - 32$; so $F = 86°$F

5. **(a) (i)** 72.25 **(ii)** 1.3 **(b)** max $-$ min $= 1 - (-7) = 8$

6. **(a)** Radius $r = 1.8 ÷ 2 = 0.9$; area $= \pi r^2 = 2.5$ m²
   (b) Perimeter $= \pi d = \pi × 1.8 = 6$ m to nearest whole number

7. **(a)** $20:50$ **(b)** 0.8 **(c)** $17 ÷ 20 × 100\% = 85\%$
   (d)(i) $800 × \frac{7}{100} = £56$ **(ii)** $50 × \frac{70}{100} = £35$

8. **(a)** $53°$ **(b)** $46°$ **(c)** $42°$ **(d)** 11

9. **(a) (i)** 5 **(ii)** 32 **(iii)** 3 **(b)** $6x + 15$

10. **(a)** $3, -1, 3, -2, 3$. Total score $= 7$
    (b) (i) $7 - (-2) = 9$ **(ii)** Let number attempted $= x$;
    so unattempted $= 10 - x$;
    $(3 × x) + (-1 × (10 - x)) = -2$; giving $4x = 8$;
    so $x = 2$ **(iii)** any permutation of: 3 correct, 4 incorrect, 3 not attempted

11. **(a)** $72° (±2°)$ **(b) (i)** $x = 180 - (90 + 37) = 53°$
    (ii) $62°$ as the triangle is isosceles
    (iii) $z = 180 - (62 + 62) = 56°$

12. Option 1: $1030 + 231.49 + 35(221.49) + 4016.50 = 13030.14$; Option 2: $1030 + 322.02 + 35(312.02) = 12272.72$; So Option 1 is cheaper by $13030.14 - 12272.72 = £757.42$

13. (a) (i) £2.63 **(ii)** £2.37 **(b) (i)** 3 **(ii)** $+6, -6$

14. (a)

	Chipped	Not chipped
Dog	14	5
Cat	10	21

(b)

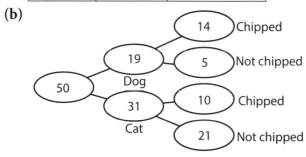

Revision Exercise 4

1. **(a)** Enniskillen and Larne **(b)** Downpatrick and Portrush **(c)** 100

2. **(a)** 12 seconds **(b)** $= 10c - 15 + 6c - 4 = 16c - 19$

3. **(a)** 4 **(b)** $3(2a - 9)$ **(c)** $-5x - 10$

4. **(a)** Equation in x: $x + x + 2 + x + x + 2 = 40$ or $4x + 4 = 40$. giving $x = 9$. AB $= 11$ cm
   (b) $600 ÷ 300 × 100\% = 20\%$

5. **(a)** $10a - 3b$ **(b)** 8 **(c)** $5(5 - 2b)$

6. **(a)** Let $x =$ length of side of square; $x^2 = 0.81$; so $x = 0.9$; Circle area $= \pi r^2 = \pi × (0.9 ÷ 2)^2 = 0.64$; $0.81 - 0.64 = 0.17$ cm²
   (b) (i) £1.52 **(ii)** £3.48 **(c)** 0.05

7. **(a)** $3a + 2b$ **(b)** $x^2 - 3x$

8. **(a)** rhombus **(b)** trapezium or parallelogram **(c)** trapezium **(d)** kite **(e)** kite **(f)** square **(g)** parallelogram or rectangle **(h)** rectangle or rhombus

9.

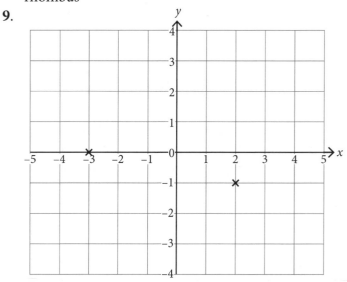

10.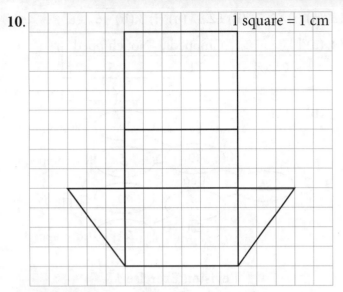

1 square = 1 cm

11. **(a)** 240 **(b)** 240 ÷ 80 = 3
12. **(a) (i)** $2x = 180 - 42$; $x = 69°$ **(ii)** $180 - x = 111°$
    (b) $2x = 180 - 53$; $x = 63°$
13. **(a)** 12 noon **(b)** 1 hour **(c)** 90 miles **(d)** 5pm
14. **(a)** 47 and 79 **(b)** 64

Revision Exercise 5

1. **(a)** £2.10 + £ 3.15 + £0.41 = £5.66 **(b)** £4.34 **(c)** 5
2. **(a)** $7.8 \times 3.4 = 26.52$ **(b)** $2 \times 7.8 + 2 \times 3.4 = 22.4$
3. **(a) (i)** 1.5 **(ii)** 10.89 **(b)** 4.91 **(c)** $150 \times {}^{20}/_{100} = £30$
4. **(a)** $15.75 + 3(4.25) = £28.50$ **(b)** Let x = number of
    additional days; so $34 = 22.75 + 2.25x$; giving $x = 5$
5. **(a)** Let x = number of black grapes;
    so $1.75 = (0.4 \times 1.85) + 0.5x$; giving $x = £2.02$
    (b) $14000 \times {}^{3}/_{100} = £420$
6. **(a)** 16 pupils ÷ 4 cans = 4 **(b)** 2.5 cans × 4 = 10
    (c) 24 ÷ 4 = 6 cans drawn opposite 'Coke'
7. **(a)**

Speed	Tally	Number
21 – 30	⊬⊬ ||||	9
31 – 40	⊬⊬ ⊬⊬ |	11
41 – 50	⊬⊬ |||	8
51 – 60	||	2

    (b) Total number of cars = 30; number of cars
    travelling > 30 mph = 21; 21 ÷ 30 × 100 % = 70%
8. Pie chart angles corresponding to order in which
    the types are listed: 72°, 126°, 90°, 18°, 54°.
9. $50p \times {}^{8}/_{100} = 4p$; so new price per litre = 50 + 4
    = 54p; 54p × 900 = 48600p = £486
10. **(a)** 10 ÷ 0.85 = 11.8, so 11 fridge magnets
    (b) 0.85 × 11 = £9.35; 10 − 9.35 = £0.65 = 65p
11. **(a)** 130.09 **(b) (i)** 57105 − 54742 = 2363 units
    (ii) 2363 × 11.02p = 26040p = £260.40
    (c) (i) $160 \times {}^{5}/_{100} = £8.00$ **(ii)** 160 + 8 = £168.00
12. **(a)** ${}^{35}/_{56} = {}^{5}/_{8}$ **(b)** 270 ÷ 300 × 100% = 90%
    (c) $\frac{1}{5} + \frac{1}{4} = {}^{4}/_{20} + {}^{5}/_{20} = {}^{9}/_{20}$ used; $1 - {}^{9}/_{20} = {}^{11}/_{20}$ left

13. **(a)** £283.32
    (b) 1066.37 − (283.82 + 150 + 80 + 320) = £233.05
14. **(a)** Lowest common multiple of 15 and 18 = 90; so
    next time = 8.00am + 90 minutes = 9.30 am
    (b) Factors of 42 = 2, 3, 6, 7, 21, 42
    Factors of 70 = 2, 5, 7, 10, 14, 35, 42
    Common factors = 2, 7
    (c)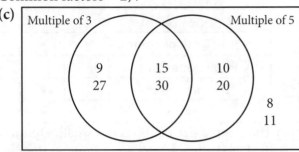
    (d) (i) ${}^{624}/_{936} = {}^{2}/_{3}$ **(ii)** 936 − 624 = 312 = 310 to
    nearest ten